D0896424

IT'S PUB TIME,
ANDY CAPP

by Smythe

A FAWCETT GOLD MEDAL BOOK

Fawcett Publications, Inc., Greenwich, Conn.

BLIMEY, THE STUFF THEY'RE PUTTIN' ON – 'ERE I AM PLAYIN' TRUANT FROM ME 'OUSEWORK TO WATCH THE SAME FILM I PLAYED TRUANT FROM SCHOOL TO SEE!

I'VE BEEN TOTTIN' UP, YOU SPEND AS MUCH ON BOOZE AS YOU ALLOW ME F' HOUSEKEEPIN'!

YER WORTH IT, SWEET'EART, EVEN IF I AM OVERPAYIN' YER

Smythe

2-15-71

REMEMBER, NOW, DON'T 'AVE TOO MANY — I KNOW WHAT YER LIKE WHEN YER GET THE TASTE

GRR! GRR!

MAN'S ALREADY NINETY PER CENT WATER, AN' STILL YER NOT SATISFIED!

Smythe 2-18-71

I'M OFF, PET—

NO INTEREST, THAT'S YOU! YER MIGHT AT LEAST SAY *WATCH YER STEP* OR *KEEP OUT OF BAD COMPANY!*

I'VE NEVER 'AD A MOMENT'S WORRY —CAN YOU IMAGINE 'IM MEETIN' ANYBODY WORSE THAN 'IMSELF?!

2-22-71

Smythe

COME ALONG NOW, MR. CAPP — I THINK IT WOULD BE BETTER IF YOU SPENT THE NIGHT WITH US

BOP!
THUMP!

YER PROBABLY RIGHT CONSTABLE. MY USUAL CELL, I PRESUME?

OH-OHH!

I'M AFRAID IT'S ALREADY OCCUPIED — WE'VE GOT A NEW MAN ON THE DESK. BUT I'M SURE WE CAN FIX YOU UP WITH ONE JUST AS NICE

DON'T GIMME THAT! YOU KNOW I'VE ALWAYS BIN 'APPY IN 302! I'VE BIN A CUSTOMER F' YEARS — I THINK I DESERVE SOME CONSIDERATION!

Smythe

SMACK

3-29-71

REMEMBER THE NIGHT WE FIRST MET, DARLIN'?

DO I?! THE BUZZIN' IN ME EARS, THE BELLS RINGIN', THE LIGHTS FLASHIN' IN ME EYES

ACTUALLY, 'E STAGGERED INTO THE PINBALL MACHINE I WAS PLAYIN'!.....KEEP IT DARK

Smythe

SEE YER LATER, CHALKIE — I PROMISED FLO I'D WALK 'ER 'OME FROM WORK

HI'YER, PET

HI'YER, KID

STAFF 'NTRANCE.

IT'S ABOUT TIME YOU PACKED THAT JOB IN, FLO

THE WAY PRICES ARE GOIN', WE'LL 'AVE TO FIND YER ONE THAT PAYS A BIT BETTER —

SORRY I'M LATE, PET, I RAN INTO TWO OLD ARMY CHUMS OF MINE—

OH, YES—?

6-15-71

YER KNOW 'OW IT IS, ONE THING LED TO ANOTHER. WE STARTED OFF IN THE 'KINGS ARMS' AND—

YES—

YES, YES—

'ANG ON, WOMAN, 'ANG ON! YER LISTENIN' FASTER THAN I CAN TALK!

Smythe

NOTHIN' T' REPORT, SARGE

I'M THINKIN' OF RESIGNIN', I 'AVEN'T 'AD ONE ACT OF FELONY IN A MONTH!

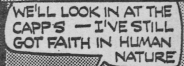

TCH! TCH! DON'T GET DISCOURAGED, SON—

WE'LL LOOK IN AT THE CAPP'S — I'VE STILL GOT FAITH IN HUMAN NATURE

Smythe

FAWCETT GOLD MEDAL BOOKS
in the ANDY CAPP series
by Smythe